1 2 3
Counting on the Farm

Brown Watson
ENGLAND

One dog

His name is Bob and he looks after the sheep on the farm.

The farmer was very cross because Bob had lost the sheep and didn't know where to find them.
"Off you go," the farmer told Bob, "and don't come back without the sheep. There are ten sheep altogether. You'll find them somewhere on the farm."

one   two   three   four   five   six   seven   eight   nine   ten

Two farm horses

These horses work hard on the farm, but today the farmer has given them a day off.

2
two

Bob asked the two horses if they had
seen the sheep. They shook their heads and
told him he should ask the three cows in the
next field. Bob thanked the horses for their help
and ran off to ask the cows if they had seen the sheep.

1	2	3	4	5	6	7	8	9	10
one	two	three	four	five	six	seven	eight	nine	ten

Three cows

3 three

Cows spend a lot of their time munching grass.
This helps them to make the milk we drink.

The three cows didn't have many visitors to their field, so they made a fuss of Bob when he arrived. They were sorry they had not seen the sheep and suggested he asked the four goats in the next field. "They often mix with the sheep," mooed a cow.

one two three four five six seven eight nine ten

Four goats

The four goats live in a field but go into their own special shed at night.

None of the four goats had seen Bob's sheep.
"I'm very glad they're not here," one goat told Bob.
"They keep us awake at night calling out 'Baa!
Baa!' to each other," another goat told Bob.
The goats said Bob should ask the pigs.

one   two   three   four   five   six   seven   eight   nine   ten

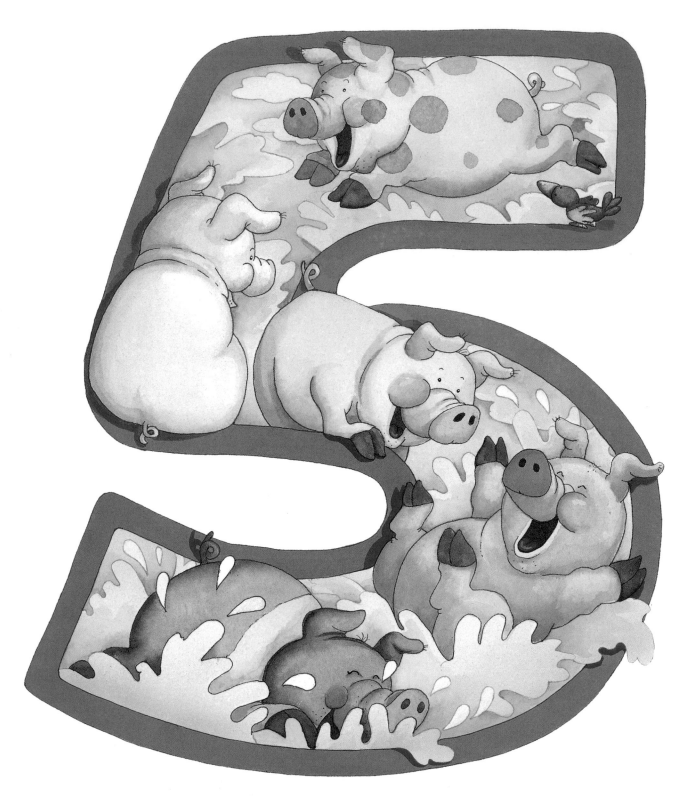

Five pigs

5
five

Most pigs are pinky-white, some are black and others have black patches or black spots.

The five pigs lived in a place called a pigsty.
They came up to the wall of their sty to speak
to Bob, but none of them had seen the sheep.
"Go and ask the rabbits," they grunted. "They see
everything going on as they nibble their lettuce."

one   two   three   four   five   six   seven   eight   nine   ten

Six rabbits

6 six

The farmer keeps pet rabbits for his children to play with. Pet rabbits live in rabbit hutches.

Bob found the rabbits in their run outside the hutch.
They told Bob they'd been too busy eating lettuce
to have seen his sheep. They told him he should ask
the farmyard cat's kittens. "They run all over the place,"
the rabbits told Bob. "They see everything!"

one   two   three   four   five   six   seven   eight   nine   ten

Seven kittens

A kitten is a baby cat. These kittens are brothers and sisters. Their mother is the farmyard cat.

The kittens were full of mischief. They wanted
to play games with Bob. He thought they were all
a bit silly. They hadn't seen his sheep anyway, so Bob
just ran off to find the hens. "Mrs Brown Hen is
very wise and is sure to help," barked Bob.

1	2	3	4	5	6	7	8	9	10
one	two	three	four	five	six	seven	eight	nine	ten

Eight hens

8
eight

Like many other farm animals,
hens can be different colours and sizes.

Bob had been right to think Mrs Brown Hen would be able to help him. Down by the pond, she had heard Mrs Duck's baby ducklings talking about the sheep. "The baby ducklings will know where your sheep can be found," Mrs Brown Hen told Bob.

one   two   three   four   five   six   seven   eight   nine   ten

Nine ducklings

A duckling is a baby duck. These are all sisters and brothers and their mother is Mrs Duck.

Bob found the ducklings with Mrs Duck,
splashing about in the pond. Bob thought the ducklings
were even more playful than the kittens – and
much more noisy, too! "Yes!" they quacked to Bob.
"You'll find your sheep in the very next field."

1	2	3	4	5	6	7	8	9	10
one	two	three	four	five	six	seven	eight	nine	ten

Ten sheep

Sheep have thick woolly coats. They are happy living outdoors and eating grass all day.

Bob had to rub his eyes when he got into the next field. The sheep were nowhere to be seen. Bob didn't know the sheep were playing a trick on him. They were in the field, but they were all hiding. Can you see where each of the ten sheep is hiding?

1 **2** **3** **4** **5** **6** **7** **8** **9** **10**

one   two   three   four   five   six   seven   eight   nine   ten

Suddenly, the sheep ran out from their hiding places. "Baa! Baa!" they cried as they chased each other in circles around Bob. The birds and the rabbits and all the other countryside animals thought it was such a funny sight.

Bob didn't think it was very funny. The sheep
ran round and round him so quickly that it
made him feel quite dizzy. He couldn't count the
sheep properly to see if they were all there.
Can you count them and see if there are ten sheep?

When the farmer counted them, there were not ten sheep. There were only nine. "One sheep is still missing," the farmer told Bob. "Off you go and find it." Can you help Bob find the way to the lost sheep?

Bob found the way to the lost sheep.
He took it back to the farmer.
The farmer added the one sheep
to the nine sheep so
that once again he had
all ten of his sheep.

Count them all to make
sure the farmer now
has his ten sheep.

The farmer told Bob he must practise counting.
He sent him to count the eggs in the henhouse.

Two eggs and **two eggs** and **one egg** make **five eggs**

2 + 2 + 1 = 5

The farmer sent Bob to count the cows in the field.

One cow and **one cow** and **one cow** make **three cows**

1 + 1 + 1 = 3

Bob then had to count all the rabbits.

Three rabbits and **two rabbits** and **one rabbit** make **six rabbits**

3 + 2 + 1 = 6

Then, Bob counted all the cats on the farm.

Three cats and **two cats** and **two cats** make **seven cats**

$$3 + 2 + 2 = 7$$

Bob counted up all the hens.

Four hens and **three hens** and **one hen** make **eight hens**

$$4 + 3 + 1 = 8$$

Finally, Bob counted the ducks on the pond.

Five ducks and **two ducks** and **two ducks** make **nine ducks**

$$5 + 2 + 2 = 9$$

Here is a picture of the farmer outside his farmhouse. His dog, Bob, is running up the lane to the farm. You can also see all the other farm animals.

Count up all the farm animals you can see in the picture.

10 sheep

8 hens

9 ducklings

2 horses

1 dog

It was the end of the day's work on the farm. All the animals had been counted, fed and made safe for the night. The farmer lay back in his favourite chair and his children gathered around to listen to a story.

His wife was busy getting their meal ready. Bob the sheepdog was really hungry after his busy day rounding up the sheep. He was looking forward to settling down in his basket for the night. The kittens would be sleeping in the kitchen with him until they were older. He hoped they wouldn't get up to too much mischief during the night!

Look at the picture and answer the questions:-

What is the number on Bob's bowl?
Can you find the seven kittens in the picture?
What number channel is on the television screen?
How many flowers are in the vase on the window sill?
How many pictures can you see hanging on the walls?
Two little mice were not invited into the kitchen,
but they are waiting patiently for any titbits.
Can you see where they are hiding?

The farmer's children went to bed and the farmer and his wife went to bed. The farmer's family and all the animals were soon safe and fast asleep. Bob the sheepdog lay down in his basket. Before he went to sleep he remembered his busy day. He remembered...

two horses...
three cows...four goats...
five pigs...six rabbits...seven kittens...
eight hens...nine ducklings...and, of course,
ten sheep – including the one that got lost!

Just to make sure he hadn't made a mistake, he closed his eyes and counted the sheep all over again.

"One sheep...two sheep...three sheep... four sheep...five sh-e-e-p...s-i-x sh-e-e-p... s-e-v-e-n sh-e-e-p...zzzzzzzzz!"

MAT

HAL